ZAPIRO

The ANC went in 4X4

Cartoons from *Sowetan, Mail & Guardian* and *Sunday Times*

David Philip Publishers
Cape Town & Johannesburg

Acknowledgements: Thanks to my editors at the Mail & Guardian *(Howard Barrell, Rehana Rossouw), at* Sowetan *(Aggrey Klaaste, Chris More, Mike Tissong, Len Maseko) and at the* Sunday Times *(Mike Robertson, Mondi Makanya) and their production staff; my assistants Anthea Lyons and Erica Haworth; my agent Debbie McClean; Marianne Thamm for bouncing ideas; all at David Philip; Nomalizo Ndlazi; and as ever my wife Karina.*

First published 2001 in southern Africa by
David Philip Publishers,
an imprint of New Africa Books (Pty) Ltd,
208 Werdmuller Centre, Claremont 7700
in association with

©2001 Jonathan Shapiro

ISBN 0-86486-502-3

Cover design by Jonathan Shapiro

Printed and bound in South Africa by
Ince (Pty) Ltd - Western Cape

For friends in New York, devastated by
unimaginable terror as this book went to print

Other ZAPIRO books

A conspiracy theorist's book is distributed by Health Minister Tshabalala-Msimang to provincial departments

7 September 2000

10 September 2000

17 September 2000   As the Olympics begin

8

26 September 2000

The most successful Games ever

28 September 2000

THE ONLY PERSON WHO, TILL THIS WEEK, HAD **NOT** SAID FERDI BARNARD KILLED DAVID WEBSTER

SOWETAN 29·9·00 © ZAPIRO

1 October 2000

5 October 2000

6 October 2000

8 October 2000

At last Yugoslavia votes him out

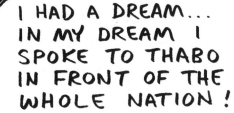

12 October 2000

©ZAPIRO's NOBEL PRIZES

12-10-00 M&G

MATHEMATICS
JAYENDRA NAIDOO
for postulating the world's largest imaginary number

R 104 billion in Arms Deal spinoffs!

PHYSICS
ROBERT MUGABE
for defying the Law of Gravity

HE JUST WON'T FALL!

CHEMISTRY
WOUTER BASSON
(uncontested)

MEDICINE
THABO MBEKI
for advances in Retroviral Science

POVERTY = AIDS

LITERATURE
HANSIE CRONJE
for various pieces of fiction

PEACE
(shared)

MILOSEVIC   MUGABE   PAGAD   ISRAELI ARMY

12 October 2000

18

HOW IT STARTED

15 October 2000

The Israeli Defence Minister's provocative visit sparks the second Intifada

18 October 2000

THE TAXPAYER'S GUIDE TO THE ARMS DEAL

THE COST...

R50 BILLION

R40 BILLION

DEFENCE DEPT.

R30 BILLION

THE SPINOFFS...

EXPECTED R104 BILLION IN COUNTER-TRADE INVESTMENT

CLINK!

AND AN EXCLUSIVE INSIDE VIEW: MAKING THE ARMS DEAL

SA OFFICIALS

ARM EXTENDED TO MAKE DEAL

ARM EXTENDED TO RECEIVE KICKBACK

SOWETAN 19-10-00 ZAPIRO

19 October 2000

Government is given free space to explain its contentious AIDS policy

19 October 2000

25 October 2000

After the Olympics, Sydney hosts the Paralympics. Team SA excels.

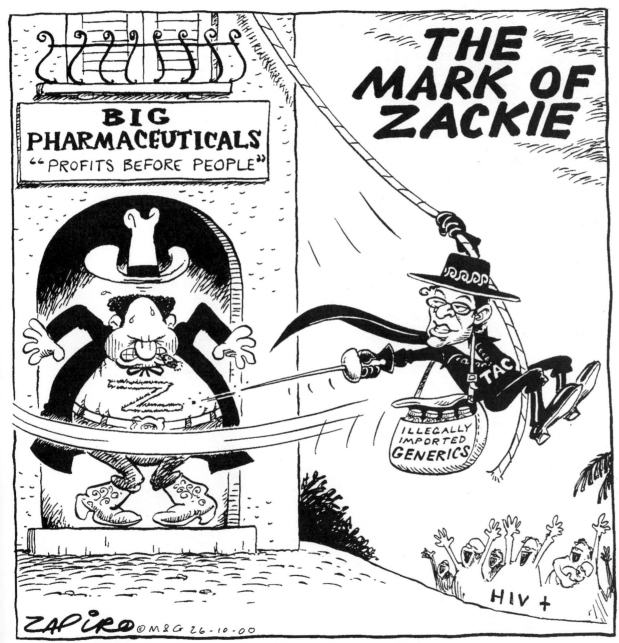

Zackie Achmat and the Treatment Action Campaign push for cheaper AIDS drugs

26 October 2000

29 October 2000   Previously fired for using the k-word in a taped phone call, André Markgraaff is re-hired

SA armaments keep landing up in conflict zones

Names, names, names! The match-fixing scandal is more serious than we thought.

2 November 2000

12 November 2000

Disputed vote count in Florida delays US Presidential Election result

16 November 2000   Whether for business or pleasure, the KwaZulu-Natal Premier enjoys spending our money

22 November 2000   Sports Minister criticizes Olympics honcho for nepotism and unbridled self-promotion

Investigations prompted by shocking footage of police setting their dogs on captured suspects for fun

24 November 2000

Three weeks after voting and still no clear winner

A probe by the Heath Unit, headed by Judge Willem Heath, is thwarted as the Constitutional Court rules a judge may not head an investigative unit

30 November 2000

5 December 2000   Verwoerdian enclave boycotts the election and holds its own whites-only vote

6 December 2000

10 December 2000

Parties still attract support along racial lines

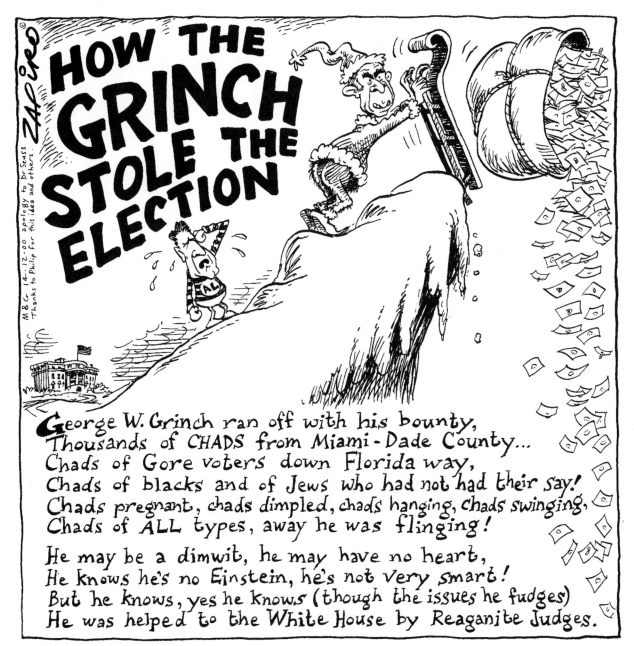

No more recounts, rules the
US Supreme Court

14 December 2000

20 December 2000

The organisers wait for thousands of whites to apologise for apartheid.

A nationwide campaign

14 December 2000

21 December 2000

GETTING AWAY FROM IT ALL, 2000

24 December 2000

10 January 2001

Now gravely ill and in a coma

17 January 2001

19 January 2001

Big winner allows publication of his name and photo

SUN. TIMES 21-1-01 ZAPIRO ©

24 January 2001

23 January 2001

After friction between government and Judge Heath, President Mbeki axes the Heath Unit
from the probe into corruption in the arms deal

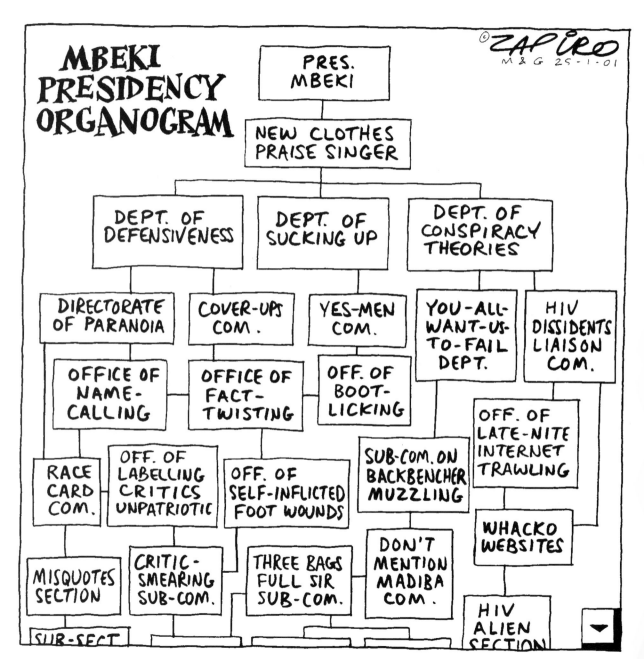

President Mbeki says an arms deal organogram drawn up by the Heath Unit shows the unit's contempt for government. Oops! …The organogram was actually drawn by the investigative magazine *Noseweek*.

25 January 2001

THE TORCH IS PASSED

Hardline militarist Ariel Sharon is elected Prime Minister

1 February 2001

7 February 2001   A bomb destroys the outspoken paper's printing press

8 February 2001

11 February 2001

The few officials who've been caught may be the tip of the iceberg

Spat over Minister Tshwete's accusation

BIG PHARMACEUTICALS

15 February 2001

22 February 2001

18 February 2001

20 February 2001

President Mbeki is away

21 February 2001   It's Budget Day. Records show Allan Boesak has called prominent people from his prison cell on an illicit cellphone.

Fractional increases for some;
nothing for others

22 February 2001

© ZAPIRO SNAPSHOTS FROM THE
SUN.TIMES 25.2.01

HAMMY AWARDS

BEST SUSTAINED WHINE:
Tony Leon

BEST GANGSTA RAP:
Bob Mugabe

BEST PORTUGUESE VOCAL:
Steve Tshwete

BEST SILENT VOCAL:
Thabo Mbeki & Dr Zuma

ZIM CRITICISM

BLUES SOLO:
"Cell in a Cell Blues"
—Allan Boesak

BEST STUCK RECORD:
"Bomb Baghdad!" — Bush, Clinton, Bush

BLUES DUO:
"Bowled Out Blues"
Judge King & Shamila Batohi

HEAVY METAL:
R 43-Billion Arms Deal

25 February 2001

28 February 2001

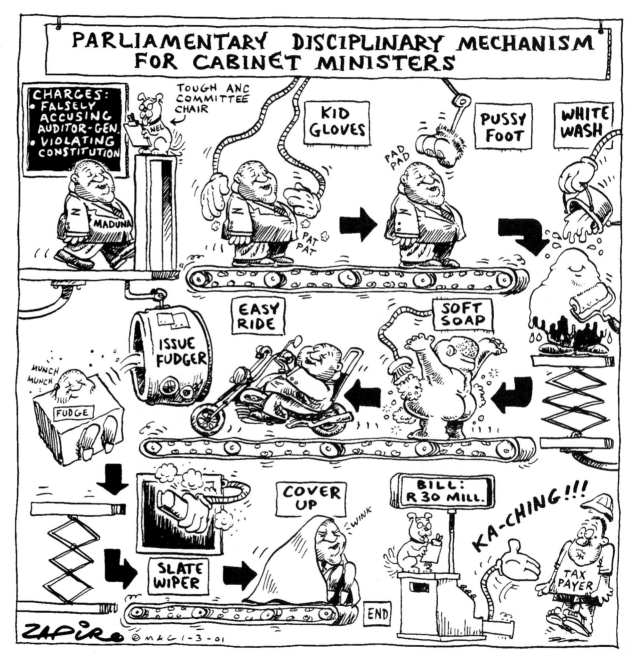

Justice Minister Maduna knew his allegation of theft was false by the time he let a R30 million inquiry proceed. Later an ANC-led committee wimps out of disciplining him.

1 March 2001

4 March 2001   A hijacking at Wonderboom Air Base turns out to be just a police exercise. Police reports mislead the world's media for hours.

WHEN JUSTICE FAILS

5 March 2001

6 March 2001   Government's legal action for the right to import generic drugs receives wide support. And it succeeds.

8 March 2001

9 March 2001   Eugene TerreBlanche's appeal against his conviction for attempted murder is turned down

ZAPIRO © M&G 8-3-01

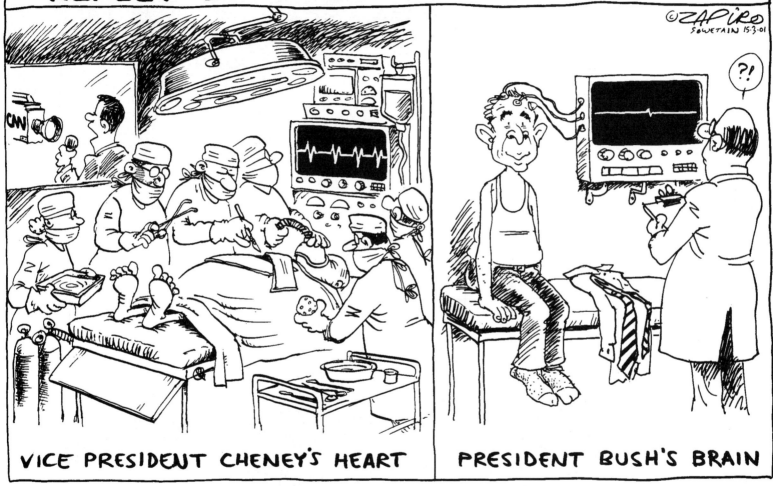

WHICH ORGAN SHOULD AMERICA REALLY BE WORRIED ABOUT?

VICE PRESIDENT CHENEY'S HEART

PRESIDENT BUSH'S BRAIN

Education Minister
Kader Asmal's vision includes
mergers of tertiary institutions

15 March 2001

20 March 2001   Warning: controversial youth programme could offend sensitive parents and teachers

27 March 2001

1 April 2001   Why did Chief Whip Tony Yengeni get a Merc 4 X 4 from a weapons company involved in the arms deal, start
financing it only after media scrutiny seven months later, and not declare this benefit to parliament? Hmmm …

4 April 2001

Botswana hangs SA citizen Mariette Bosch

5 April 2001

22 March 2001

R 2,5 million into the expedition, Dr. Dolittle wondered whether **pushmi-pullyu** had been the ideal way to travel.

The inclusion of dissident scientists in the Presidential AIDS Panel was bound from the start to result in a divided final report

5 April 2001

10 April 2001

11 April 2001

15 April 2001

43 soccer fans are crushed to death at Ellis Park

Ticket sales, security measures and crowd control have been bungled

19 April 2001

22 April 2001

Books by anti-apartheid writers Nadine Gordimer and Njabulo Ndebele are among those deemed racist and patronising by zealous Gauteng officials

from "WILDLIFE OF ZIMBABWE":
"...revelling in the stench of the great beast's mouth, the small bird picks out scraps for re-digestion."

25 April 2001

A plot against the President?
Or just the dubious allegations
of one discredited source?
Minister Tshwete is convinced
enough to finger prominent
ANC cadres Cyril Ramaphosa,
Tokyo Sexwale and Mathews
Phosa.

25 April 2001

THE **REAL** THREAT OF HARM TO THE PRESIDENT

26 April 2001

The plot could cause the President 'actual physical harm,' says Tshwete

29 April 2001

2 May 2001

100

3 May 2001

STEVE LOSES THE PLOT.

6 May 2001   President Mbeki admits it was a mistake to name plot suspects

10 May 2001

Yet another mine disaster

9 May 2001

Ignoring requests to come and tell them how he got that 4X4

10 May 2001

The Media
vs.
President T.M.Mbeki

It's another plot! We've discovered the Media are actually the Ku Klux Klan!

Everything is all the Media's fault!

Mr President, you are the greatest! You are the most beautiful! (grovel grovel, fawn fawn, bow, scrape, curry favour and pass the gravy please)

Patriots! Join us in our heroic mission: Shoot the messenger!

This space paid for by the A-List

SUN.TIMES 13·5·01

13 May 2001 · A group of black businesspeople run an advert alleging a media conspiracy against the President

16 May 2001

So why did they take the drug companies to court?

15 May 2001

Herschelle Gibbs and others bust in Antigua

20 May 2001

Support from Helen Suzman

17 May 2001

17 May 2001

22 May 2001

24 May 2001

25 May 2001

Apparently the DA leader has presidential aspirations

23 May 2001   Some ANC-friendly rulings around the arms deal blemish Frene Ginwala's fine record as an impartial Speaker

30 May 2001

29 May 2001
US Secretary of State on his African visit

31 May 2001

3 June 2001   Strange coincidence: Strijdom monument and the square itself collapse on this particular day

Nkosi Johnson
1989 – 2001

Champion of the
New Struggle

5 - 6 - 01
SOWETAN
ZAPIRO ©

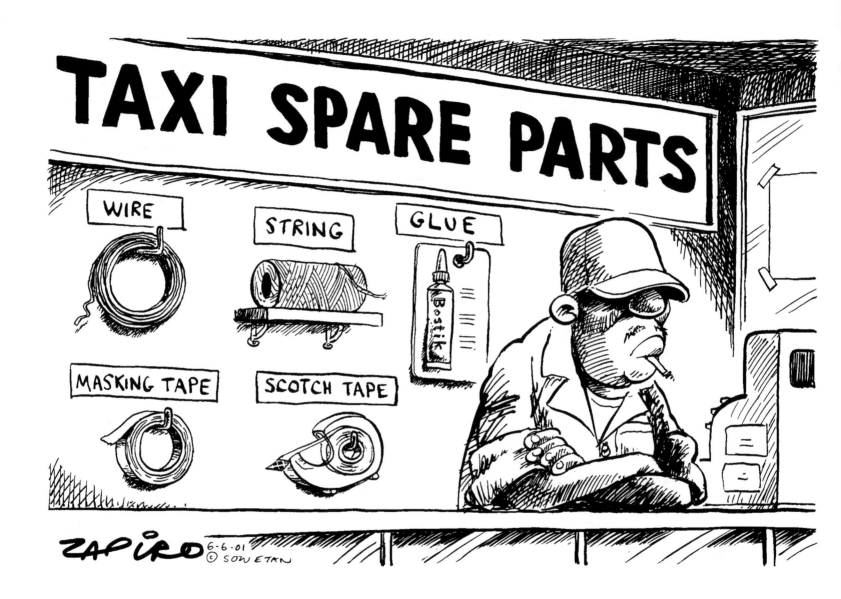

6 June 2001

Investigation of a fatal taxi accident reveals brakes repaired with wire

10 June 2001

Death of the leader of the so-called 'war veterans'

12 June 2001   Owed a lot in arrears, Eskom imposes indiscriminate power cuts

THE FAITH GAZA HANDBOOK ON HOW TO GET FIRED

14 June 2001

17 June 2001   In his two years as head of SAA, the departing CEO was paid a whopping amount

ANC GIVES PRES. MBEKI SURPRISE PARTY — Report

20 June 2001

Last week at a rally the President, irked by Winnie's typically late grand entrance, had pushed her and knocked her hat off as she went to embrace him

128

BAD IMAGE CREATED BY THE OLD UNRELIABLE CRIME STATS

IMPROVED IMAGE EXPECTED FROM UPCOMING ACCURATE CRIME STATS

21 June 2001

Solar eclipse week. Mayor Pieter Marais is implicated in falsifying petitions to fake public support for his unpopular street-renaming scheme.

21 June 2001

Evidently Tony Yengeni is only one of 30 state officials and politicians who got special deals on luxury cars from EADS, a company that won a big contract in the arms deal

5 July 2001

10 July 2001   At Bredell, desperate people are being sold plots at R25 each by PAC officials who don't own the land

Evicted

12 July 2001

12 July 2001

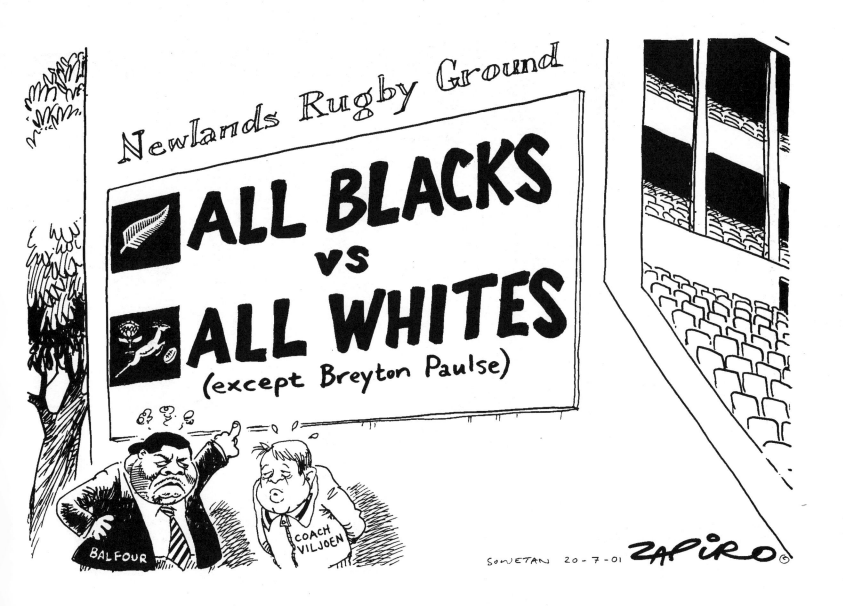

29 July 2001

31 July 2001   Fifteen white parents charged with racial assault go free due to botched prosecution

2 August 2001

2 August 2001

After recent footage of a beached whale's demise
9 August 2001

8 August 2001   The US threatens to boycott the conference in SA if reparations for slavery and Zionism as a form of racism are to be discussed

12 August 2001

Pressure results in a watered-down document

16 August 2001

19 August 2001

"PIETER MARAIS IS HERE TO COMPLAIN ABOUT YOU CALLING HIM A FAT PIG AND THE PIG IS COMPLAINING ABOUT BEING ASSOCIATED WITH PIETER MARAIS."

21 August 2001

Cracks in the Democratic
Alliance

23 August 2001

26 August 2001

28 August 2001   Fearing job losses, workers prepare to strike against privatisation. Tripartite Alliance tension mounts.

Govan Mbeki, 1910–2001

29 August 2001   Days before the World Racism Conference in Durban, US Secretary of State Colin Powell reflects
White House pique over the agenda by announcing he'll boycott

30 August 2001

6 September 2001   Walkout over hostility to Zionism is an attempt to derail the conference. It fails.

6 September 2001

THE NATIONS HAVE COME...

THE ISSUES HAVE BEEN SPOTLIGHTED...

SLAVERY	NATIVE AMERICANS
COLONIALISM	AUSTRALIAN ABORIGINALS
ZIONISM	ROMA PEOPLE
CASTE SYSTEM	ECONOMIC RACISM
TIBET	AIDS RACISM
ENVIRONMENT	KURDS
...ISM	SUDAN SLAVERY
	ARAB SLAVERY
	XENOPHOBIA
	GENDER RACISM

U.N. RACISM CONFERENCE

THE DEBATE HAS BEEN VIGOROUS...

...AND THE FINAL DECLARATION HAS BEEN LOADED WITH ENOUGH LEGAL DISCLAIMERS FOR EVERYONE TO GO HOME UNACCOUNTABLE FOR PAST OR PRESENT ABUSES.

9 September 2001   By week's end, racism is declared a crime against humanity and Europe offers an apology for slavery

13 September 2001